Save the Puppies!

SIMON AND SCHUSTER/NICKELODEON

D1361243

SIMON AND SCHUSTER
First published in Great Britain in 2010 by Simon & Schuster UK Ltd
1st Floor, 222 Gray's Inn Road, London WC1X 8HB
A CBS Company

A CIP catalogue record for this book is available from the British Library

ISBN 978-1-84738-971-8
Printed in Great Britain

10 9 8 7 6 5 4 3 2 1

Visit our websites: www.simonandschuster.co.uk
                    www.nickjr.co.uk

¡Hola! I'm Dora and this is Boots. We're playing a video game called 'Save the Puppies'. Do you want to play, too? Press the red button to start.

oh no! The Dogcatcher is chasing all the puppies in Doggy Town. He's locking them in Doggy Cages.

But **look,** one puppy is **escaping!**

He's jumped right out of the game. **¡Hola, Perrito!** Hello, Puppy!
Don't worry, you're safe with us. Hey Boots, I think he wants us to save the
other puppies. We need to jump into the game and help him.

We're inside the game! But how do we find the puppies? Who do we ask when we don't know where to go? That's right, Map! Shout 'Map'!

Map says we go through the Doghouse and down Dog Bone River to get to the Doggy Cages. The Dogcatcher has hidden **100 keys** in **red** boxes along the way. The keys will open the cages. So, look out for the **red** boxes!

Hey, wait! Can you see four stars? We need to jump and catch them. Everybody jump! Higher! **1, 2, 3, 4** stars to put in my Star Pocket! One of the stars is called Saltador. He's a super-jumping Explorer Star.

'WOOF, WOOF!' I think the puppy is trying to tell us something – he can see a **red** box. Quickly, Boots, jump on the box to let the keys out. How many did we get? Count with me!

1, 2, 3, 4, 5, 6, 7, 8, 9, 10!

Count and follow with your finger!

1 2 3 4 5 6 7 8 9 (10) 11 12 13 14 15

Look, there are two more boxes. Each box has **10** keys inside.
How many keys do we have altogether? Let's count ten at a time.
We already have ten so now we start at **11** and count up to **20**.

Great. Now count from **21** to **30**. Good counting!

16 17 18 19 20 21 22 23 24 25 26 27 28 29 30

Now, where did Map tell us to go first? Through the Doghouse, that's right! We need to go in one side and out the other to get through. Come on, let's crawl in through the doggy door. **Oof,** it's a tight squeeze!

Which door will take us out the other side? Look at the screen above the door. We need to find the door with a matching bone picture. Which is the right door? The **green** one, right!

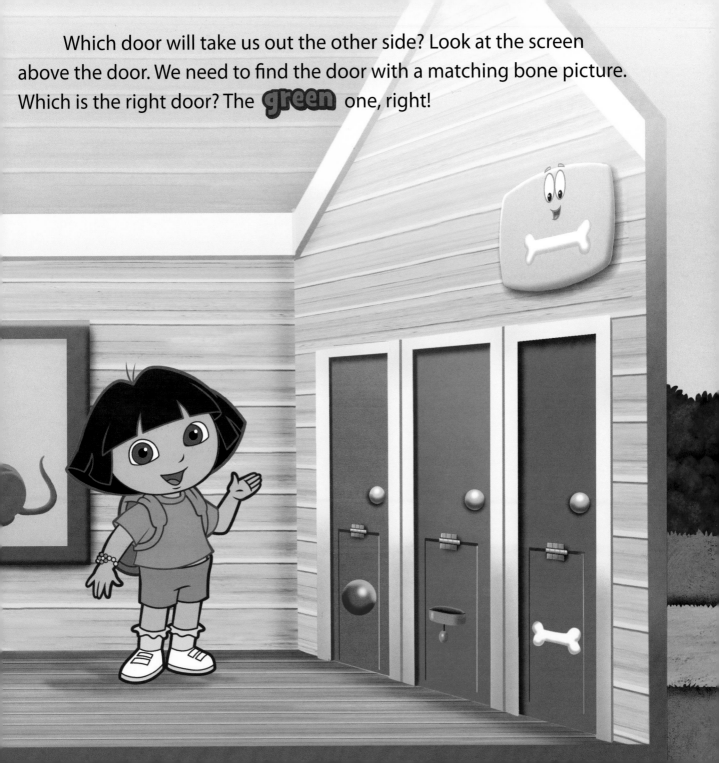

What's that noise? **uh-oh,** it's the Dogcatcher! He is chasing us. We need to close the door fast. The door speaks Spanish so we need tell it to close in Spanish. Say "cierra"!

Count and follow with your finger!

3I 32 33 34 35 36 37 38 39 40 4I 42 43 44 45

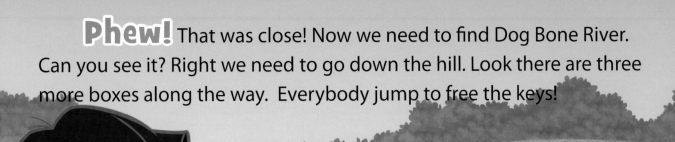

Phew! That was close! Now we need to find Dog Bone River. Can you see it? Right we need to go down the hill. Look there are three more boxes along the way. Everybody jump to free the keys!

There are ten keys in each box so let's count ten at a time. We had **30** keys already so start at **31** and count to **40**. Great! Then count from **41** to **50**. One more box to go... count from **51** to **60**. ¡Fantástico!

46 47 48 49 50 51 52 53 54 55 56 57 58 59 60

'WOOF, WOOF!' Look! The puppy has sniffed out another box! It's buried in the ground so we need to dig it up. Come on everybody, let's dig like the puppy!

DIG! DIG!

DIG!

Count and follow with your finger!

61 62 63 64 65 66 67 68 69 70

Dig, DIG!

WOW! This box has **20** keys in it – that's two lots of ten!

We had **60** keys before so now we need to count up from **60**. Let's count ten at a time. Start at **61** then count to **70**. Then count from **71** to **80**. Good work! Now we have **80** keys.

71 72 73 74 75 76 77 78 79 80

We went through the Dog House and now we need to go down Dog Bone River. All aboard the Doggy Paddle Boat!

Put on your life jacket and jump in, too! ¡Vámonos, let's go!

Oh no! The Dogcatcher is right behind us.

We need to sing a Doggy Song to make the boat go faster. Everybody sing 'Woof, woof, woof'! **Woof, WOOF, WOOF!**

We did it, great doggy singing! We made it down Dog Bone River just in time. Hey, look what puppy has found – another box of keys. Let's count them. Can you remember how many we had already? **80**, That's right! So start at **81** and count to **90!**

Count and follow with your finger!

81 82 83 84 85 86 87 88 89 (90)

Hooray! We're at the Doggy Cages but we need **100 keys** to free the puppies and we only have **90**. Can you see a red key box?

Of course you do, it's a **GIANT** box!

But how will we jump high enough to open it?

I know! Saltador the Explorer Star can help us do super-high jumps! Are you ready? Let's **jump!**

Wheee! We found the last ten keys! Let's count them up and check we have **100**. Remember start at **91** and count up. Yay, **100!** The keys are opening the cages and the puppies are **escaping!**

91 92 93 94 95 96 97 98 99 (100)

Hey, look, even Dogcatcher is happy that the puppies are free.
He says he is going to get a new job – as a postman!